SHIRE NATURAL

G000049825

# PARASITIC WORMS

## JIM FLEGG

## CONTENTS

COVER: *Aphelenchoides attacking fungal mycelium.*

Series editors: Jim Flegg and Chris Humphries.

Set in 9 point Times roman and printed in Great Britain by C. I. Thomas & Sons (Haverfordwest) Ltd, Press Buildings, Merlins Bridge, Haverfordwest, Dyfed.

# Introduction

What *are* parasitic worms, technically called nematodes, or, to give them their popular name, eelworms? They are a group of relatively lowly multi-cellular animals, simpler than earthworms and much less elaborate than shellfish or insects, for example. Their common name gives an impression of their shape, for most are slender and thread-like. They range in size from the microscopic — mere fractions of a millimetre — to 8 metres (26 feet) or more in length, but the vast majority are less than 5 millimetres (¼ inch) long. Although worm-like, they are not related in any way to the earthworms (Annelida) that we find in gardens, and their nearest relatives are probably the tapeworms, flatworms and flukes. All the various names for these parasitic worms — nematodes, helminths (a predominantly American term), roundworms, eelworms — may be met with in various publications. Throughout this book they are used interchangeably. Students of them may be nematologists, helminthologists or parasitologists.

Nematodes, or eelworms, are extraordinarily widely distributed. They have been found in soils high on mountains, in the ooze deep on the ocean floor, in the Arctic ice cap and even in such unlikely habitats as stale vinegar and fibre beer mats. Most animals and plants have eelworm parasites, and there are many that inhabit their 'hosts' without causing any damage, or where there may be mutual benefit (symbiosis) — the eelworm assisting with digestion, in return for shelter. Countless millions of eelworms are involved in the natural cycle of breakdown of dead plant material in the soil. An American nematologist, Nathan Augustus Cobb, writing in 1914, summed up eelworm distribution very neatly: 'if all the matter in the Universe except the nematodes were swept away, our world would still be dimly recognisable. We would find its hills, valleys, rivers, lakes and oceans represented by a film of nematodes.' And as many of the plant and animal parasites infect only one host species, he could have added that most, if not all, of the animals and plants on our world would also be recognisable, at second hand, by their eelworm parasites.

Eelworm anatomy, though efficient and sometimes elaborately evolved, is basically simple. Nematodes have a flexible but strong cuticle, which although

*The position of nematodes in the animal kingdom.*

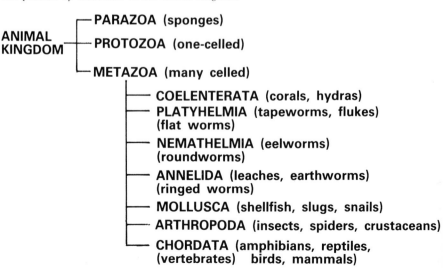

ANIMAL KINGDOM
- PARAZOA (sponges)
- PROTOZOA (one-celled)
- METAZOA (many celled)
  - COELENTERATA (corals, hydras)
  - PLATYHELMIA (tapeworms, flukes) (flat worms)
  - NEMATHELMIA (eelworms) (roundworms)
  - ANNELIDA (leaches, earthworms) (ringed worms)
  - MOLLUSCA (shellfish, slugs, snails)
  - ARTHROPODA (insects, spiders, crustaceans)
  - CHORDATA (amphibians, reptiles, (vertebrates) birds, mammals)

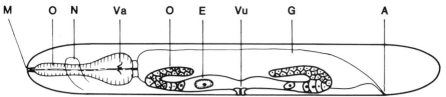

M    O  N    Va     O  E   Vu      G          A

Fig. 1. *A generalised female eelworm, showing the arrangement of major organs within the body.* M, *mouth;* O, *muscular oesophagus;* N, *nerve ring (the nervous coordination centre);* Va, *oesophageal valve;* G, *gut;* O, *ovary and oviduct (paired in this example, sometimes there is only one);* E, *egg;* Vu, *vulva and vagina;* A, *anus.*

Fig. 2. *A photograph from a scanning electron microscope of the head end of Hemicy-cliophora, a plant-parasitic eelworm, showing the 'lips' round the mouth and the ring-shaped ridges on the cuticle.*

Fig. 3. *The mouth and 'lips' of Acrobeles, found round plant roots in sandy soils but probably not actually a plant parasite. The photograph was taken on a scanning electron microscope and appears here magnified about two thousand times life size: the elaborate lips are actually about 0.025 mm long.*

commonly covered in tiny ridges is not segmented as in the earthworms. This cuticle contains body fluids under some pressure, and the combination functions as a hydro-elastic skeleton (as in the earthworms), as these are animals without a rigid backbone — or indeed many other rigid parts. At the front is a mouth, sometimes just a simple tube, sometimes elaborately developed for filtering food from passing water currents or for sucking blood or sap. This is connected by a muscular pumping oesophagus to a simple tubular gut, and this in turn to an anus closed by a sphincter muscle. There is a network of radial and longitudinal muscle bands with a very simple nervous system controlling them and producing an S-shaped eel-like wriggling movement, which is how eelworms move about. In essence, almost all eelworms

swim through their environment, whether it be the blood (or sap) or intestinal contents of their host if they are parasites, or in the film of moisture between soil particles if they live free. Though some eelworms respond to light, few have proper light receptors ('eyes') of any sort and, though practical, their sensory systems (usually allowing response to temperature and various chemical signals) are elementary when compared to those of higher animals. Plant-parasitic eelworms living in soil and looking for a plant root on which to feed seem to seek it by snake-like waving movements of the head, where the sensory organs, called amphids, are located. Plant roots emit a variety of chemical exudates, and it is these the eelworms detect, moving always towards the strongest concentrations, which occur

3

Fig. 4. *The head-ends (mouthparts and oesophagus) of various types of eelworm: S, a 'saprobic' or bacterial feeder, with a simple tubular mouth and muscular oesophagus (with a conspicuous non-return valve); P, a predatory Mononchid, with a large mouth capsule armed with a sharp tooth and a muscular oesophagus giving powerful suction; Do, a Dorylaim, the group containing virus vectors, with a simple tubular stylet used for plant feeding in some, bacterial or animal feeding in others; Ty, a Tylenchid. This group contains the most sophisticated plant parasites, characterised by a stylet with basal knobs and an oesophagus with several digestive glands.*

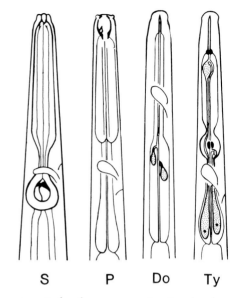

**S**     **P**     **Do**     **Ty**

nearest the root. In this way, if they stray from the shortest route, the 'scent' gets weaker and so they turn back again, drawn almost as if by a magnet to their target.

Eelworms have reproductive organs in what might seem to us to be an impressive array of varieties. Some have males and females and reproduce sexually, while others may have both sexes in the same individual ('hermaphrodite'); yet others may have no males at all ('parthenogenetic'), or may change (usually at the onset of unfavourable environmental conditions) from parthenogenetic to bisexual reproduction. Most species lay minute eggs, sometimes containing a well developed embryo, while others give birth to active young stages. The basic pattern of development (although some species omit or condense some of the stages) is of an egg, followed by four or five juvenile or larval stages of steadily increasing size, these stages each separated by a moult when the old skin is cast off after a new larger one has grown crinkled up beneath it, until finally the adult stage is reached.

Thus the 'average' eelworm looks like a minute, transparent and rather long sausage, capable of wriggling along, eel-like, in a thin film of moisture. Few nematodes have any natural colouring but the larger they are the whiter they appear. Few have much protection, either. Their cuticle, though strong and impermeable for its size, is of little help in resisting drying out in an air current, so inevitably most eelworms are denizens of damp sheltered places in the outdoor world. The parasites have the natural shelter offered by their host, but even these are at risk when transferring from one host to the next — the process of infection.

Some eelworms, however, show adaptations allowing them to survive periods of climatic adversity (for free-living species) or vulnerability (for transferring parasites). The simplest of these is shown by plant-parasitic eelworms of the genus *Aphelenchoides,* which includes pests of strawberry and chrysanthemum. As autumn approaches and plant growth slows towards a standstill, the eelworms gather in a mass in sheltered crevices in the plant and gradually dry out almost completely. In this form, called 'eelworm wool', their life processes too are almost at a standstill, making little detectable demand on their energy resources. Eelworm wool will remain viable for months, and occasionally years, 'coming back to life' surprisingly quickly as soon as it

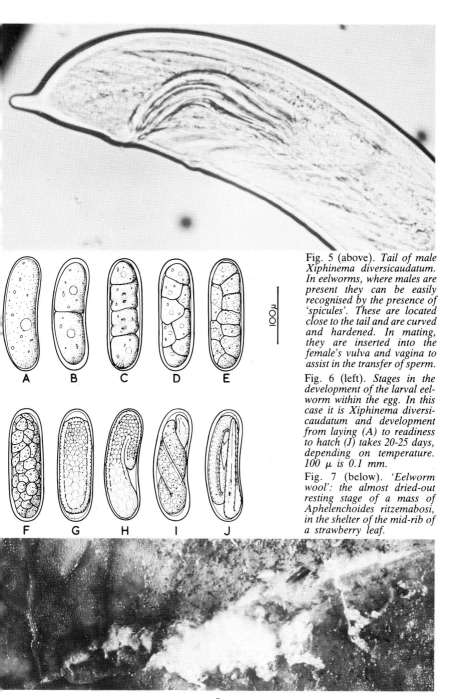

Fig. 5 (above). *Tail of male Xiphinema diversicaudatum. In eelworms, where males are present they can be easily recognised by the presence of 'spicules'. These are located close to the tail and are curved and hardened. In mating, they are inserted into the female's vulva and vagina to assist in the transfer of sperm.*

Fig. 6 (left). *Stages in the development of the larval eelworm within the egg. In this case it is Xiphinema diversicaudatum and development from laying (A) to readiness to hatch (J) takes 20-25 days, depending on temperature. 100 µ is 0.1 mm.*

Fig. 7 (below). *'Eelworm wool': the almost dried-out resting stage of a mass of Aphelenchoides ritzemabosi, in the shelter of the mid-rib of a strawberry leaf.*

encounters a drop of moisture. Others, like the animal parasites of the genus *Ascaris*, have a very thick-shelled egg and at the egg stage can resist most adversities that nature or man may pit against them, including boiling water and many 'disinfectant' solutions. Of the plant parasites, the cyst-forming species have the best developed resistant stage, when the eggs are protected until the next season within the swollen dead and tanned skin of their mother, which is called a cyst.

Are there many eelworms? Compared with other groups of animals, they are little studied, but the probability is that there will turn out to be even more species of eelworm than there are of insects. Actual numbers of individuals can be prodigious: a cupful of earth from a garden, for example, is likely to contain several thousand nematodes. Some of these will probably belong to undescribed species, 'new to science' as it is called, even though they originate so close to home.

Our lack of detailed studies of eelworms as a whole is surprising, because man has known about them for perhaps three thousand years, or maybe even longer, and even the most primitive of early men was at least aware of his eelworm parasites, even if he could not identify them. Among the first zoological records are references to the Guinea worm, *Dracunculus,* thought to be the 'fiery serpent' that attacked the Israelites, recorded in the Bible in Numbers 21, 6-9. This and the common large 'roundworm' of man, *Ascaris,* that lives in the intestine and occasionally passes out with the faeces, are referred to in Egyptian papyrus writings dating from about 1500 BC. Hippocrates and Aristotle, writing in Greece a few centuries before the birth of Christ, comment on 'worms' in horses (even at this distance in time readily recognisable as *Oxyuris equi*) and dogs. From then until the middle ages numerous herbalists suggested remedies for 'worm' infestations, ranging from simple enemas to empty the intestines of worms and all to supposedly more specific treatments from which plant names like 'worm-seed' and 'wormwood' derive, names still in use today.

In general the animal-parasitic eelworms are so large that they were easily seen (if not felt) by the ancients, but it was not until the nineteenth century that they were properly studied with the aid of microscopes. Our first information on the vast range of 'free-living' eelworms comes from 1656, when a zoologist called Borellus first observed 'vinegar eels' — the tiny eelworm *Turbatrix aceti,* which at that time was present in almost all vinegar. Held up against the light, these microscopic organisms could be seen swimming in great swarms, sparkling with reflected light.

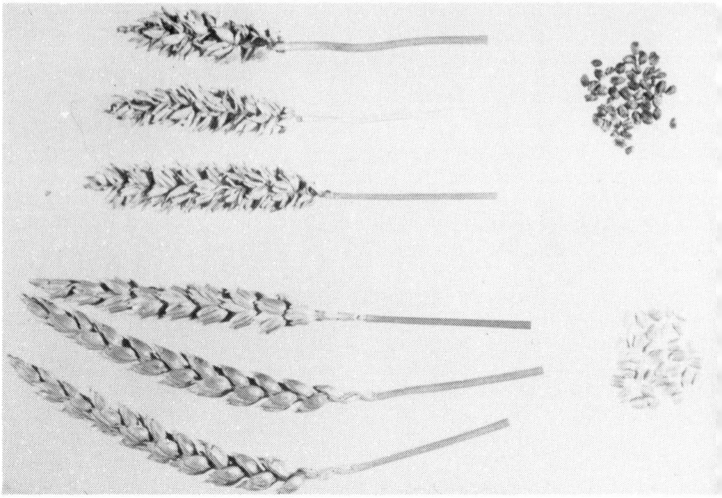

Fig. 8. *Wheat infected by Anguina tritici, the cause of 'corn cockle'. Above, the shortened ears and dark malformed seeds due to cockle; below, healthy ears and grain.*

6

William Shakespeare unwittingly provided the first record of plant-parasitic eelworms, when, in about 1594, he wrote in *Love's Labour's Lost* 'sowed cockle, reap'd no corn'. Almost 150 years later, an English Roman Catholic priest called Turbeville Needham crushed one of these shrunken 'cockles' (blackened wheat seeds) in a drop of water under his primitive microscope and was amazed to see, wriggling out, a mass of 'worms, eels or serpents'. In a letter written in 1743 to the Royal Society and published in their *Philosophical Transactions*, he wrote: 'Upon opening lately the small black Grains of smutty Wheat, which they here distinguish from blighted Corn, the latter affording nothing but a black Dust, into which the whole Substance of the Ear is converted; I perceived a soft white fibrous Substance, a small Portion of which I placed upon my Object-plate: It seemed to consist wholly of longitudinal Fibres bundled together; and you will be surprised, perhaps, that I should say, without any least Sign of Life or Motion. I dropped a Globule of Water upon it, in order to try if the Parts, when separated, might be viewed more conveniently; when to my great Surprise, these imaginary fibres, as it were, separated from each other, took Life, moved irregularly, not with a progressive, but twisting Motion, and continued to do so for the Space of Nine or Ten Hours, when I threw them away. I am satisfied that they are a species of Aquatic Animals, and may be denominated Worms, Eels or Serpents, which they very much resemble.'

Because it contains a clear suggestion of 'spontaneous generation' of life, Needham's letter created ecclesiastical uproar, and the poor man was placed under such pressure by his church superiors, who considered his view heretical, that he had eventually to retract his statement.

Thus, rather arbitrarily, the eelworms — or nematodes — can be divided into three groups: animal parasites, plant parasites, and free-living forms. Fascinating as they are zoologically, the free-living eelworms have been overshadowed by the high social and economic importance of their parasitic relatives.

# Parasites of animals

Parasitic roundworm infections of man and his domestic animals are horrifyingly widespread. They are not confined, as might be supposed, to less technologically developed areas of the world, where hygiene is poor and where remedial drugs are too expensive or not available, though both animal and plant parasites do seem to occur more widely in tropical regions and the diseases caused, especially to man, by tropical parasitic worms seem both more dramatic in their symptoms and more devastating in their effects than worm infections in the highly developed countries of northern Europe, for example, with their well fed populations. However, relatively innocuous worm infections, particularly of children, are widespread, even commonplace, in these developed countries, and even here they should not be treated too lightly. *Trichinella spiralis*, the pork trichina worm, can be lethal to man eating poorly cooked infected pork, as can a worm (whose true host is a seal) which is occasionally transmitted to man via the herring, often eaten uncooked (just soused in vinegar) in Scandinavian countries. And despite modern hygiene, there are still disturbing numbers of cases of blindness in children caused by a roundworm infection (*Toxocara canis*) obtained from the family pet dog.

In the late 1940s an American parasitologist, Dr Richard Stoll, made some estimates of the numbers of humans infected with various parasitic roundworms. Working on an estimated world population of about 2000 million people, he calculated that over 600 million were infected with *Ascaris lumbricoides*, the large roundworm, over 450 million with the hookworms *Ancylostoma* and *Necator*, and almost 200 million with *Wucheraria*, which causes the terribly disfiguring disease elephantiasis. Although far better drugs (called anthelminthics) are now available, their cost has inhibited widespread use in the poorer countries of the world, where an already densely crowded population, living in conditions ideal for

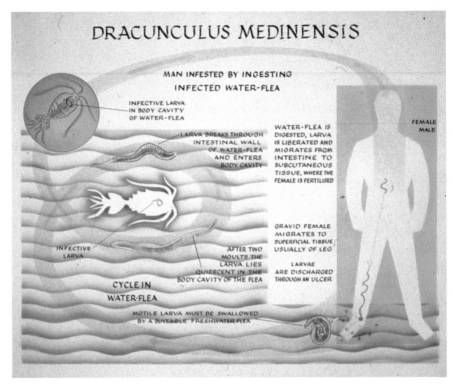

Plate 1. *Diagrammatic life cycle of the Guinea worm, Dracunculus medinensis.*

the spread of nematode infections, has increased dramatically since then, so little improvement would be expected today.

Parasitism, often, and understandably, evokes in humans a feeling of revulsion, but it is a fascinating mode of existence, demanding a wide range of unusual adaptations. In many cases satisfactory theories to account for the evolution of parasitism are exceedingly difficult to construct, as a review of a selection of typical animal-parasitic nematode life cycles will show.

Many of the Ascarid nematodes, often called roundworms, parasitic in mammals and birds, including man and both wild and domesticated animals, have a relatively simple life cycle. The adults of *Ascaridia galli*, a parasite of chickens, dwell in the small intestine of their host, absorbing food through their body wall and often not causing too great a problem except where malnutrition is a complicat-

ing factor. The eggs pass out and remain, protected by a thick shell, on vegetation or on the soil surface until eaten again by a host. Within the egg the larval worm hatches and undergoes two moults, so when the infective egg is swallowed it is a second-stage larva (or juvenile) that emerges, to moult three further times before reaching adulthood. The larval stages mature in the cavity of the gut, sheltering between the folds of the wrinkled lining of the intestine wall. The adult moves out free into the gut, matures as it feeds and eventually produces eggs: so the cycle is complete.

The large stomachworm of sheep, *Haemonchus contortus*, has a broadly similar life cycle, but here the egg hatches soon after reaching the ground in the droppings of the sheep. The egg is minute — less than one hundredth of a millimetre long — and the emergent larva feeds on bacteria while sheltering, and

8

# WUCHERERIA BANCROFTI

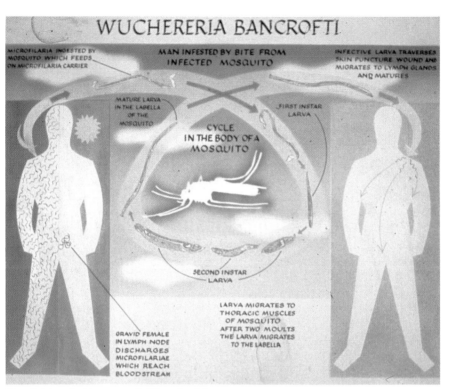

Plate 2 (above). *Diagrammatic life cycle of the filarial worm, Wucheraria bancrofti.*

Plate 3 (right). *The microfilaria of Wucheraria in a blood film, magnified several hundred times.*

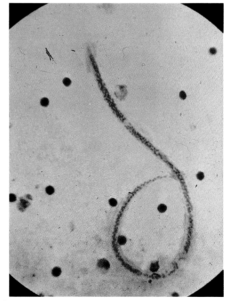

growing, within the dung. This is a hazardous time for such a tiny organism and mortality must be high, but as the adult female within the gut of the sheep is laying (in typical parasite fashion) up to ten thousand eggs daily there is ample compensation for the losses. At its second moult the larva retains, as a loose protective sheath, its previous skin and moves up on to the grass blades, there to await being eaten, to reinfect another sheep. The development from egg to infective larva takes a few days, depending on climatic conditions, and this provides one way of reducing infection without recourse to expensive drugs. If, depending on the weather, sheep are moved to a fresh pasture every four to seven days and the original pasture is 'rested' for a couple of weeks or more, the chances of the flock picking up a reinfection from its own droppings are considerably reduced.

*Ascaris lumbricoides*, the large round-worm, one of the commonest parasites of man and pigs, has a life cycle partly very similar to that of *Ascaridia galli*. It has resistant eggs, within which an infective larva develops. In man the commonest means of reinfection, or transfer of infection, is on unwashed hands following defecation. Once eaten, the egg hatches and the life cycle begins to show differences. The larva burrows through the gut wall, to be carried in the blood supply through the liver and heart to the lungs, where further larval development occurs. Fourth-stage larvae travel up the wind-pipe and then back down the oesophagus into the gut once again, where they mature and begin to lay eggs.

The life cycle of the hookworm *Ancylostoma* is more complex. Also a dweller in the small intestine, the adult hookworm seizes a section of the gut wall in its fearsome mouthparts and sucks blood, often causing considerable trouble. Once the hookworm has taken hold, the flow of blood through its body never ceases, as it extracts its own food supply from the blood as it passes through its gut. Though hookworms are small (10 to 20 millimetres long — around ½ inch) there

may be many of them, and the continuous blood loss causes anaemia and debilitating weakness in the unfortunate host, often severe in nature and opening the way for other infections. The eggs the adult females lay pass to the outside world and hatch and can either infect a fresh host which inadvertently eats one, or — as a major step forward in the development of parasitism — they can burrow through the skin of the host (an unshod human foot, for example).

As in *Haemonchus*, the third-stage larva is the infective one, sheathed in the protective second-stage cast skin. The sheath is cast as it penetrates the skin (or is eaten). Having penetrated the skin, the larvae circulate in the blood stream through the heart to the lungs, where they bore out again and wriggle up the windpipe and down into the intestine, where the cycle starts again with the development through the remaining larval stages to adulthood.

*Trichinella spiralis*, the pork Trichina worm, shows yet another adaptation to parasitism in the animal roundworms: the cyst. This offers protection during the period of transfer from one host to the next, when the parasite would normally be exposed to the hazards of life in the outside world. *Trichinella* is a parasite of a wide range of meat-eating animals, many of them with a fairly broad choice

Fig. 9. *Photomicrograph of a cross-section of a hookworm head attached to the wall of the small intestine. Note the firmly grasped plug of tissue in the mouth.*

of diet, like the pig, the rat, the badger and man himself. For roundworms, these are small: the males 1.5 millimetres and the females about twice this. As adults, they live in the wall of the duodenum and may cause digestive upsets like sickness and diarrhoea. This, though, is not the main problem.

Female *Trichinella*, instead of laying their eggs, retain them in the body cavity, where they hatch, so they give birth (a process called ovo-vivipary) to live young — yet another example of reproductive flexibility in parasitic worms. These larvae, liberated in the gut wall, find their way first into lymph vessels and then into the veins. They travel with the blood, first to the liver and then to the heart, and then from the heart to the lungs, where they transfer from the venous blood to the oxygenated blood. Within this blood stream they are returned to the heart and pumped out with the arterial blood supply, which carries oxygen to all parts of the body. Many are lost in the process, and many reach unsuitable tissue and die, but others reach suitable muscles, where they grow. In reaction, the muscle forms around them a fibrous capsule, or cyst, lemon-shaped and about half a millimetre long. Here the larva must stay, coiled in a spiral (the *spiralis* of its scientific name) until the flesh is eaten and the cyst wall digested away by the next host. This event is a rarity in man now that cannibalism has largely died out, but commonplace where infected farmyard rats are eaten by pigs, which in turn are likely to be eaten by man. Historically, it could have been rats eaten by wild boars, and the wild boars eaten by bears.

Favoured muscles for encysting include those operating the jaws, shoulders and legs, but others, including those between the ribs and operating the diaphragm, essential for breathing, are also targets. In the past, when more uncooked meat was eaten, the incidence of *Trichinella* in man would have been much higher, but today it is very low except in primitive circumstances (Eskimos in the Arctic suffer severely, for example) because of thorough cooking and effective meat inspections.

The protection that the parasite achieves during the transfer stage from one host to the next is a very valuable advance in the evolutionary history of parasitism. In the case of *Trichinella* the cyst protects an otherwise extremely vulnerable larval stage from the hazards of the outside world, hazards which can only be met in the less elaborately evolved parasites by the production of enormous numbers of eggs or larvae. Plenty of these simpler strategist parasites are still flourishing, so although their method is very wasteful it does work.

Other animal parasites have taken the 'protected transfer larva' a stage further by the introduction of a mobile 'intermediate host' into their life cycle. Evolutionarily, one of the simplest of these is to be seen in *Syngamus trachea*, the 'gape worm' of poultry, which has relatives affecting cage and aviary birds and birds in the wild. *Syngamus* has another unusual feature: once adult, the two sexes meet in the windpipe (trachea) of their host, and then lock together in permanent copulation. The male is usually less than 5 millimetres (0.2 inch) long, the female longer at up to 20 millimetres (0.8 inch), and together they resemble the letter Y. Here they are generally debilitating, especially if the infestation is large, and cause coughing fits and shortness of breath (accompanied by a gaping action of the beak), and occasionally the unfortunate host may asphyxiate with a blocked windpipe.

*Syngamus* eggs are laid in the windpipe, then pass up it in mucus during coughing and are swallowed, to pass through the digestive tract and emerge in the droppings. Here the larva develops — still within the egg shell — to the third stage. Then the egg is infective and may be eaten by a new host. More often, and here is the novelty, the egg is swallowed by one of the many small soil invertebrate animals, usually a slug, snail or annelid worm. Within this intermediate host the eggs hatch, and the larvae penetrate the gut wall to encyst in the body cavity. Here they can survive for many months, without developing further, before the slug (or other animal) is eaten by a bird. Once the slug is digested, the larva is liberated and a new infection ensues. As there is no larval development within the second (invertebrate) host, it is

Plate 4. *Moving sheep regularly from pasture to pasture helps limit parasitic worm infections, as on Romney Marsh, a traditional sheep-rearing area in Kent.*

Plate 5. *An adult Mermis, white and thread-like, climbs slowly up the stem of a Hebe flower. Her eggs, laid on the leaves, will be eaten by grasshoppers or beetles, which the developing worm larva will eventually destroy. Other parasitic worms are now used in biological control of insect pests.*

Plate 6. *Carrots attacked by Meloidogyne, appropriately called the 'root-knot eelworm' and one of the world's most damaging crop pests.*

Plate 7. *An apple root swarming with the ectoparasite Trichodorus. The eelworms are about 1 mm long, and the ginger colour of parts of the root surface indicates areas they have damaged.*

perhaps most accurate to describe the slugs, snails and worms as 'transport hosts'.

It is but a step from this process to the involvement of the intermediate host much more fully, and often very sophisticatedly, in the life cycle of the parasite, serving to spread it more widely than would otherwise be the case. The tropical filarial worms of the genus *Wucheraria* are an excellent example. The adults are parasitic in the glands and lymphatic system of man and cause a grotesquely unpleasant enlargement of the tissue, usually in the legs, arms and sexual organs, called elephantiasis. The first-stage larvae, called microfilariae, circulate in the surface blood vessels, from which they are extracted by blood-sucking flies or mosquitoes. The larvae grow and moult in the muscles of the intermediate host and at the third stage migrate to the mouthparts of the insect, from which they re-infect man when next the insect sucks blood. In man they pass through the gut wall into the blood and lymph vessels and there mature. There is one further amazing development in the sophistication of this parasitism. There are various types of filarial worm. In one (for example *Wucheraria*) the first-stage larvae appear in the superficial blood vessels only at night: for these, the intermediate host is a night-flying mosquito. In another (for example *Loa*) the larvae circulate only during the day and for this the intermediate host is a day-flying Tabanid horsefly. Thus the chances of the microfilaria and its appropriate intermediate host (perhaps better called a 'vector') meeting are maximised, though the mechanisms of the various timings of filarial appearance in blood vessels near the skin are still not properly understood.

The Guinea worm *Dracunculus* shows a pattern of parasitism of even greater complexity. Man is infected, in tropical areas, by drinking untreated water containing small Copepods (or water fleas). These Copepods are numerous and widespread, and some will have been infected as intermediate hosts by *Dracunculus* larvae. Once accidentally swallowed, the *Dracunculus* leave the dead Copepod and migrate through the human gut wall into connective tissue, often in the legs. Here they mature, lengthening greatly. As she

Fig. 10. *Extraction of a Guinea worm wound round a stick at a medieval apothecary's 'surgery'. (From Velschius, 1674.)*

14

matures, which may take more than a year, the female becomes packed with thousands of eggs, which hatch while still inside her body. At this stage the nematode moves towards the skin, causing a large blister there, accompanied by a powerful burning sensation, hence the 'fiery serpent' reference in the Bible. The logical way to relieve this pain is to put the affected area in water, when the sudden chilling causes the blister to burst and the head of the Guinea worm to rupture, liberating the larvae into the water. Here they are swallowed by Copepods, and so the cycle starts again.

The only way of extracting Guinea worms is to pull them out slowly from the blister. This must be done over several days as the nematode may be a metre (3 feet 3 inches) long. The area surrounding the nematode is naturally inflamed and may be easily susceptible to a secondary bacterial infection, which can cause severe problems. Even worse, should the *Dracunculus* break during the extraction process, the formation of scar tissue or even some calcification around the length of the remnant may cripple the host. In the past, the nematode was wound round a small stick, which was then fixed close to the wound ready for more winding next day. It has been argued that this is the likely origin of the first symbol of the British Medical Association, a branch with 'serpents' twined around it.

Animal parasitism is not confined to man and his farm animals. Like the higher animals, insects too have their nematode parasites, and some of these are being studied by research workers seeking alternatives to more toxic pesticides or to control intractable insect pests of man's crops. One such parasite is amongst those most often seen by the man in the street. Often called 'thunder worms' because of their tendency to climb wet plants or wriggle around in puddles after thunderstorms, these nematodes are several centimetres long, very slender and thread-like, and white or grey in colour. A typical example would be a *Mermis* species. The females (it is these that are seen, full of eggs, after thunder) lay their eggs on leaves, and the leaves are eaten by insects like grasshoppers, locusts, Colorado beetles and weevils, all sometimes damaging pests and all difficult to control with conventional pesticides.

Within its insect host the *Mermis* egg hatches, and the developing larva penetrates into the body cavity, often heading for the sexual organs. Often the parasitised insect is killed outright, or at least effectively sterilised, thus providing good control. Researchers are now seeking ways of increasing parasite numbers in cultures, especially for smaller kinds of nematode than *Mermis*, some of which are even more damaging because they carry bacteria also lethal to the insect. Also needed will be effective techniques for spraying the parasites in water on to crops in need of protection so that costly, environmentally dangerous or simply ineffective agrochemicals can be withdrawn.

# Plant-parasitic eelworms

Eelworms that live on or in plants are generally much smaller than their animal-parasite counterparts. Whereas the latter are often big enough to be visible to the naked eye, some being several centimetres or more in length, very few of the plant parasites are longer than a millimetre or two. Thus they are practically invisible, being transparent as well as minute, and the poor growth or disease that they cause has consequently often long been as puzzling to the farmer or scientist as those caused by bacteria and viruses.

As with animal-parasitic worms, not all eelworms kill the plants they feed on. It is a measure of the efficiency of any parasite that it can thrive while not destroying its host, and the more efficient plant-parasitic eelworms cause their host plants little damage. This is to their advantage, as the longer the host stays alive, the longer it continues to provide the eelworms with food. But many, perhaps most, of the plant-parasitic eelworms, even if they do not kill the plant, debilitate it severely. If a field of crops is under

Fig. 11. *Development of the stylet in a larval Xiphinema. In A, a special cell lays down the first larval stage stylet, and once this is complete, begins to lay down its replacement for the second larval stage (B). When the larvae moult, their mouthparts are shed along with the discarded skin, and the new stylet moves forward. 50 μ is 0.05 mm.*

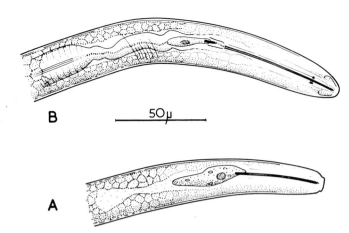

B

50μ

A

attack by eelworms, this generally becomes apparent because of conspicuous bare or poor patches, roughly circular in shape, scattered across the field. Several eelworms are economically very important and, especially in the tropics, may devastate a crop. This is particularly important when the local economy is heavily dependent on a single major export commodity like cotton, tobacco or bananas.

Most, though not all, plant-parasitic eelworms live in the soil and attack the roots, the others invading stem, leaf, flower or fruit tissues. They have several features in common (parasitism has arisen in a number of diverse groups) but of these the most conspicuous is the possession of well developed mouth parts. These generally take the form of a protrusible stylet, sometimes called a 'spear', which resembles a sort of tooth and is more properly called an odontostyle. Normally the odontostyle is hollow and finely pointed, and it functions in many ways like a hypodermic needle. The eelworm approaches a plant cell and penetrates the cell wall by pushing out its stylet, using powerful muscles attached to its base. Once the cell wall is pierced, digestive juices from the oesophagus are pumped in to liquefy and partly digest the contents. Then the muscular bulb in the oesophagus, working like a pump and fitted with a tiny horny 'non-return' valve, sucks the cell contents back through the hollow stylet and down into

the eelworm's gut for digestion.

The damage that eelworms cause to plant tissues ranges from the almost invisible to distortions and swellings as grotesque as the damage caused to human tissues by elephantiasis. Plant cells often react to damage by turning brown and woody, as part of a mechanism used by the plant in an attempt to restrict the damage to one zone, a process akin to the use of watertight doors to isolate compartments in ships. In some cases large pieces of the outer, less important layers of a root will fall off. In other cases the damage is far more sophisticated. The digestive juices, and the enzymes they contain, of some plant-parasitic eelworms are very closely adapted to their host. Some families of eelworms, notably the cyst formers and those responsible for disorders like 'root knot', use these enzymes to manipulate the host to their advantage. In such cases the adult female eelworm is sedentary and feeds in just one location on the root. Within the root tissues her enzyme secretions provoke the formation of 'giant cells' near to her head. These greatly enlarged cells are full of sap rich in sugar and other nutrients, and it is on these that the eelworm feeds and grows with no need to exert itself any further than protruding its stylet to take a meal.

Yet another range of crop damage possibilities results from the association of eelworms with other agents of plant disease. The open wounds on the root

16

Plate 8. *Close-up of the crown of a strawberry plant, so damaged by feeding Aphelenchoides fragariae, the strawberry eelworm, as to be useless.*

caused by some eelworms may be swiftly invaded by harmful soil microbes. In other cases the association is more formal: cauliflower disease of strawberry, which reduces the crown of the plant to a cauliflower-like and useless mass of tissue, is caused by an eelworm (*Aphelenchoides ritzemabosi*) and a bacterium acting together, neither causing nearly as much damage on its own. Many of the extremely important wilting diseases of a wide range of crops, caused by soil fungi, are also much worsened by the involvement and interaction between the fungus and particular eelworms.

Because of the resemblance of their mouthparts to a hypodermic needle, some of the plant-parasitic eelworms are economically important not in their own right, but as transmitters (vectors) of diseases caused by the smallest of all disease agents, the viruses. In much the same way that yellow fever, a virus disease of man, is transmitted by blood-sucking mosquitoes from one person to another, so too can eelworms suck virus-infected sap from one plant root and infect the plants that they feed on subsequently.

In general the 'normal' plant-parasitic eelworm life cycle differs little from those of the animal parasites. The female lays eggs, males sometimes being involved in their fertilisation, sometimes not, depending on species. These eggs are normally not protected, though some are laid within plant tissues, and others (the cyst eelworms) within a protective case. From the eggs larvae hatch and grow through a series of moults, usually four, before they reach adulthood. The whole process occupies from a few weeks to a few months and tends to be appreciably faster in warm climates, allowing much greater rates of increase in eelworm numbers and consequently much greater eelworm problems in tropical countries. In summary, the general pattern of a parasitic life style (as in the animal parasites) is a relatively short life span, with several generations each year or season, and with a very high productivity of eggs to cover losses due to the hazards of finding a suitable host.

There are exceptions to this general rule, mostly in two groups associated with virus transmission, *Xiphinema* (called 'dagger nemas' in the United States)

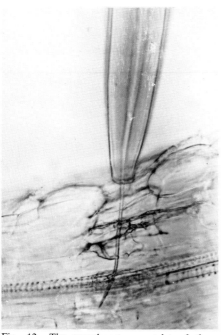

Fig. 12. *The mouthparts or stylet of the virus-transmitting Xiphinema plunged deep into root cells. The tubular cells showing spiral bands near the stylet tip are responsible for fluid transport through the plant and are ideal for the spread of virus infection. The stylet is about 0.1 mm long.*

and *Longidorus* (called 'needle nemas'). These are amongst the largest of plant ectoparasites, some reaching 15 millimetres (0.6 inch) in length. They can sometimes be found in freshly broken clods of earth, looking like tiny white wriggling rootlets. Though they do not possess a protective resting stage like a cyst, these eelworms exhibit astonishing endurance, some being able to survive in the soil, without any plant roots present, for upwards of two years. Presumably this is in a state of torpor, with the bodily processes functioning at a much reduced rate. Even more remarkably for creatures so small, they lay eggs sometimes only once a year, and then perhaps only thirty or so of them, early in the summer. They may take two or three years to reach adulthood and can live to the age of five or even six years.

Plant-parasitic eelworms and the free-living eelworms that live in the soil have many natural hazards to survive. The soil is just as hazardous an ecosystem as are the African plains. Instead of lions and antelopes as predators and prey, the various soil animals fill these roles. The prey are the eelworms, facing potential predators that include some of the worms, soil mites, beetles and other small carnivorous soil animals. In addition, some eelworms themselves are fearsome predators on others of their kind. Armed with a toughened, funnel-shaped mouth and a very powerful muscular oesophagus capable of exerting considerable suction pressure, these hunters wriggle through the soil in search of their victims, chosen indiscriminately and even including small specimens of their own species. Should they come close to prey, it is sucked into the mouth and sliced open on a vicious thorn-like tooth, and the body contents are emptied from its skin and digested.

Not only the animal kingdom provides hazards for eelworms: fungi, although lowly members of the plant kingdom, are also effective predators. Some have developed specialist adaptations to this mode of life and possess tacky pads on which eelworms stick if they brush against them in passing. The fungus then penetrates the trapped eelworm with hyphal threads, which slowly digest its body contents. Other fungi form a network of hyphal threads through the soil, every so often throwing off a lasso-like process. The cells in these hyphal nooses react extremely quickly should an eelworm poke its head into one: they swell and constrict round the victim, which once again is penetrated by other hyphae and digested.

Plant-parasitic eelworms can be divided into two broad types, depending on how they live. Some live outside the plant and feed on the surface cells, or deeper if they have long stylets: these are called ectoparasites and tend also to be migratory, moving about through the soil from plant to plant. Others, called endoparasites, spend all or most of their life cycle deeply buried inside the plant tissue.

An excellent example of an endoparasite is the potato cyst eelworm, *Globodera rostochiensis*, a major scourge of gardeners who try to grow potatoes in the

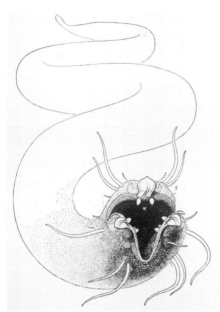

Fig. 13. *A fearsome view of a predatory Enoplid eelworm. Enoplids range in size from 2 to 5 mm and most occur in marine habitats. (From N. A. Cobb, USDA Yearbook, 1914.)*

Fig. 15. *The head end of an endoparasitic eelworm Pratylenchus within a plant root cell, the walls of which are showing signs of damage. The stylet is short, about 0.02 mm long, dark and dagger-shaped, and is guided by a ring of horny tissue.*

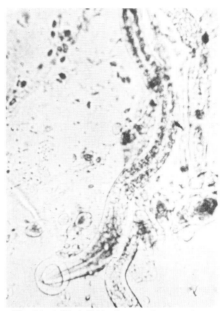

Fig. 14. *A Rhabditid eelworm about to place its head in the noose formed by a constricting ring of the predatory fungus Dactyella.*

Fig. 16. *A tangled mass of the endoparasitic Pratylenchus, each about 0.5 mm long, in an apple root. Darkened cells are the first signs of damage due to their feeding.*

Plate 9. *In vineyards patches of poor growth indicate the possibility of an eelworm-transmitted virus disease. Within this French vineyard, symptoms of eelworm and virus damage are obvious in the stunted yellow vines.*

same soil year after year. This species has an intriguing life cycle. Juveniles invade potato roots and move through the cells as endoparasites, feeding continuously. The juvenile females then settle in one spot and produce secretions that cause the potato root to develop giant cells around their heads. The females feed on these cells, hardly needing to move their heads as they do so. They grow enormously, eventually expanding so much that, by the time they mature, they burst out of the root tissue.

The males, meanwhile, have matured and left the plant in search of a female that has just burst out of the root. Fertilisation takes place and the female dies. However, instead of decaying, her skin turns into a delicate leather-like bag — the cyst — that harbours the eggs. These cysts are visible to the naked eye and look like pinhead-sized nodules on the surface of the root. The eggs can remain safe within the cyst, for several years if needs be, until a potato root passes by close enough to stimulate the cyst chemically into hatching. The cycle then starts afresh.

Another cyst eelworm, *Heterodera schachtii*, was amongst the first of the plant parasites to be studied in any detail. The sugar beet industry was developed,

largely in Germany, early in the nineteenth century, and during that century sugar production from beet expanded rapidly. A German research worker called Schacht, writing in 1859, indicated the tremendous economic potential of eelworm damage when he described a disease of sugar beet that was causing serious losses in German beet fields. Other workers identified the cause of the problem as *Heterodera schachtii* and set about devising control measures. Beet cyst eelworm remains a problem to this day and, despite the tremendous advances in chemical pesticides since the nineteenth century, the first practical control recommendation — a crop rotation allowing several years between beet harvests — is still perhaps the principal technique for limiting damage.

Of the eelworms attacking the above-ground part of the plant, one of the most widespread is the stem-and-bulb eelworm *Ditylenchus dipsaci*. This is an endoparasite and causes considerable distortion of the plant tissue and heavy crop losses. It, too, was one of the first plant parasites to be identified, when in 1857 it was isolated from the heads of teazel plants (*Dipsacus*, hence the eelworm's name). At that time teazels were of considerable economic importance in the carding (combing out) of wool prior to spinning, but nowadays *Ditylenchus* problems are most important in crops of broad beans, onions and flowering bulbs like daffodils and narcissi.

The strawberry eelworm *Aphelenchoides fragariae* is another eelworm that attacks the stems, flowers and leaves and which may seem to be an endoparasite but is not. It feeds as an ectoparasite on the developing leaves and flowers in the heart of the crown of the strawberry plant. Protected by the folds in the tissues and by layer upon layer of leaves, it is as well protected against predators and pesticides as an endoparasite. Strawberry eelworm damage usually manifests itself in a stunted plant with distorted, dwarf leaves and very few, if any, flowers. Strawberries are propagated by runners, and the runners for commercial plantings come from a small number of specialist nurseries, which produce runners by the million. The runners originate in the crown of the plant, and when the parent plants become infected with *Aphelencoides* the consequences can be disastrous. At low population levels they cause no symptoms and can easily pass undetected, to be spread widely during propagation. Given good conditions for multiplication — probably a cold spring followed swiftly by a warm summer is best — the eelworms rapidly became a problem, destroying fields of strawberries almost completely.

Most ectoparasites, however, are soil dwellers. There are very many of them, both of species and individuals. Most are parasites of wild plants or weeds, rather than of man's commercial cultivars and crops. Damage caused by ectoparasites (other than the virus vectors) is often difficult to detect and assess and may show as severe symptoms only occasionally, for example in a year of drought, when eelworm damage to the plant's root system impedes its ability to take up what water there is, and the eelworms cause the final damage that kills the plant. Sometimes, like *Trichodorus viruliferus*, they produce striking symptoms. *Trichodorus* tend to gather in huge spaghetti-like masses around the tips of some of the larger structural roots of apple trees. Although less than 1 millimetre long, they can damage the superficial layers of cells around the growing point, or meristem, to such an extent that growth may cease and the root die.

The means of spread of eelworm parasites of crop plants is a matter for concern. Endoparasites within plants (*Aphelenchoides* in strawberry for example) spread easily from one field to the next, and even internationally now that plant material is sold so widely. In the past, even well meaning schemes set up to provide developing countries with stocks of new planting material were the unwitting dispensers of disease — for example caused by the eelworm *Radopholus*, which was artificially spread in this way throughout the tropics in banana plants. Plant health inspections and certificates, issued by inspectors from the appropriate country's Ministry of Agriculture, should nowadays go a long way to limiting spread by this means. More locally, many nematodes must be spread from field to field on farm implements and tractor wheels. Yet others will be spread in seed, and others still, like the cyst eelworms with their resistant stage, may be blown around almost like dust.

But for some the problem is more intriguing — the virus vectors *Xiphinema* and *Longidorus* for example. These are ectoparasites with no resistant stages, and furthermore they are primarily parasites of the roots of trees in old, rather damp woodland, only coincidentally and occasionally becoming pests of crops like raspberries, strawberries and hops, when these are planted close to woods or hedges, or on soils from which the woodland or hedgerows have been cleared in the fairly recent past. But the intriguing part starts further back in time.

Some ten thousand years ago, most, if not all, life over much of Britain was wiped out during the last ice age. It is easy to imagine how most animals returned to Britain, and also how plants re-established themselves, once the ice cap had retreated northwards again. But studies have shown that populations of these eelworms rarely expand faster than about a metre (3 feet 3 inches) a year, wriggling unaided through the soil, and this is much too slow for them to have returned to Britain between the end of the ice age and the severing of the British Isles from continental Europe a few thousand years afterwards.

The eelworms must have taken some giant strides to reach Britain, and they must have been rapid because the nematodes would not have survived for more than a few days in dry soil. It may be that they were helped by birds, whether long-haul migrants or species that inhabit woodlands with muddy soils, particularly if they probe deep into such soils for their food. An ideal candidate for such a transport job is the woodcock. It lives in woodland throughout the year; it loves damp areas, walking around and probing the soil there for food, so it would pick up nematodes on its beak and feet, and it migrates, pausing on its way in suitable woodland to feed itself up for the next stage of its journey. Once a woodcock had carried the first of these eelworms into Britain, other birds and animals would have spread them around, as would streams and brooks washing away the open soil and banks (and with them the eelworms) after a heavy fall of rain. All that remained was for the expanding population of man to come along later and cut clearings in the woodland for agriculture, and the eelworms were there already, waiting to take advantage.

# Finding and studying eelworms

Not long ago, the use of a hand lens or a small microscope was commonplace among those interested in natural history, and in particular by those concerned with the study of pond life, which was once one of the most popular of all hobbies. Today, however, naturalists are able to be far more mobile, while birdwatching has become the most popular hobby. At the same time various national and local conservation groups, trusts or societies have emerged and expanded, and many people devote their spare time to this more practical aspect of natural history. Thus the interest in smaller plants and creatures, and in more detailed observations of them, has waned, to be replaced by a more organised 'collective' approach to natural history as a hobby.

Filming these small organisms creates great problems, and in consequence they appear only very infrequently compared with other groups of animals in the spectacular range of wildlife films presented on television. This may help account, perhaps in considerable part, for an apparent lack of enthusiasm for microscopic wildlife.

But these forms of life are fascinating, and if the Victorians were able to study minute creatures, surely so too can we. Much of the equipment needed is easily obtained or simple to make, and only hand lenses and especially microscopes are expensive.

For the study of both plant and animal parasites, much of the equipment needed is similar. Generally, higher-powered lenses and microscopes will be more useful for plant parasites, lower powers for the usually larger animal-parasitic worms. Scalpels, best obtained with interchangeable disposable blades, can often be bought in model shops or at laboratory equipment suppliers, and the latter will be able to supply various types of forceps (or tweezers in everyday life). Those tweezers used domestically for extracting splinters or unwanted eyebrow hairs are often perfectly practicable. A good supply of glass microscope slides and cover slips will be necessary (obtainable from laboratory equipment suppliers), as will a range of dishes and buckets, some of the dishes reasonably delicately made and of glass, so that suspensions of extracted eelworms (and other things) can be examined.

Although the topic may seem macabre, it is only right to explain how to find animal parasites. The parasites of man and larger farm animals are best left to the experts, but parasitic worm eggs, and occasionally larval stages, can often be found in the droppings of smaller mammals, and particularly birds, if these are broken up, in water, beneath a low-powered microscope or high-powered lens. Normally this is not such an obnox-

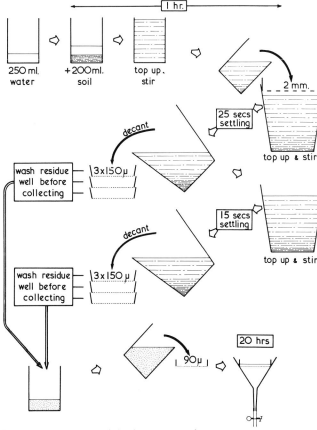

250 ml.
water

+200ml.
soil

top up,
stir

1 hr.

2 mm.

25 secs
settling

top up & stir

wash residue
well before
collecting

3×150μ

decant

15 secs
settling

top up & stir

wash residue
well before
collecting

3×150μ

decant

90μ

20 hrs

Fig. 17. *Diagrammatic representation of the decanting and sieving technique for extracting eelworms from soil. For smaller eelworms, rather longer settling times may be used, and for practical purposes the second decantation may be omitted. A single sieve of 150 micron (0.15 mm) mesh aperture is normally adequate.*

ious operation as might be supposed.

The best source of adult parasites is freshly dead animal road casualties. The commonest victims are hedgehogs, rats and a variety of birds. The corpse must be freshly dead or the parasites inside may have started to be damaged by digestive juices or decay. Fresh corpses are also much less smelly. In essence, the parasites are dissected out of the various organs in this post-mortem examination, which is best carried out on a wooden board. Scalpel, sharp-pointed scissors and forceps allow the organs, particularly the various sections of the gut, to be removed. They are best opened out in a dish of water, or even better of saline (kitchen salt) solution. Then the worms can be teased out of the gut contents, or released from their hold on the gut wall,

using forceps and fine needles. Once separate, they can be examined with a lens or microscope. Step-by-step students' guides to the dissection of various animals (usually the rat and the pigeon — but these are usefully general-purpose) can be obtained from educational booksellers.

Extracting eelworms from plant shoots or roots, or from soil, is much easier. What is needed for plant material is either a funnel or a shallow dish full of water, in which a fine-mesh sieve can stand on little legs. The plant material is washed first to remove any soil and then chopped up with scissors (as if it were being made into mint sauce) on to the sieve. The sieve is then placed in the water and left for twenty-four or forty-eight hours, when it is removed. Any

23

plant-parasitic eelworms present will have wriggled out and through the sieve and be in the water. To concentrate them, the water in the dish can be poured into a measuring cylinder or a large test tube and allowed to settle for a few hours. Then the uppermost three-quarters can be smoothly and carefully decanted and rejected, as the eelworms will have sunk into what remains. This is then examined under a microscope. For closer examination, eelworms can be sucked up in a drop of water in a pipette and placed on a microscope slide. If they are too active, gentle warming over a candle flame will relax them for better observation under higher magnification.

To extract nematodes from soil, a similar approach can be adopted, placing the soil sample on a high wet-strength tissue on the sieve. For the best results, the soil layer, well crumbled, should be only a few millimetres thick and must not be jogged once in position. Alternatively, and rather more sophisticatedly, the processes set out in the diagram for a decanting and sieving technique can be followed. Only rarely would it be necessary to use the full programme, as normally a single stirring up would suffice. The sieve mesh sizes and timings shown are to extract larger eelworms, like the virus vectors. For smaller species, a longer settling time can be allowed, but a finer-mesh sieve will be needed. Sieves can be bought from laboratory suppliers or home-made with bolting cloth. The figures given are for the dimensions of the holes in the sieve, which are usually approximately square. The symbol μ is for microns, which are units of one thousandth of a millimetre. Once again, the extracted eelworms can be finally 'concentrated' by allowing them to stand in a measuring cylinder or test tube.

## FURTHER READING
There are no compact field guides to the parasitic worms, either of animals or plants. But there are books which give details of identification, host ranges and life cycles, and much else besides, so they make valuable additional reading. A selection follows:

**General**
Croll, N. A. *The Ecology of Parasites*. Heinemann, 1966.
Croll, N. A. *The Organisation of Nematodes*. Academic Press, 1976.

**Animal parasites**
Baer, J. G. *Ecology of Animal Parasites*. University of Illinois Press, 1952.
Crofton, H. D. *Nematodes*. Hutchinson, 1966.
Lapage, G. *Parasitic Animals*. Heffer, 1958.
Lapage, G. *Veterinary Parasitology*. Oliver and Boyd, 1956.

**Plant parasites**
Goodey, J. B. *Soil and Freshwater Nematodes*. Methuen, 1963.
Southey, J. F. *Plant Nematology*. HMSO, 1970.
Thorne, G. *Principles of Nematology*. McGraw-Hill, 1961.
Wallace, H. R. *The Biology of Plant Parasitic Nematodes*. Arnold, 1963.
Wallace, H. R. *Nematode Ecology and Plant Disease*. Arnold, 1973.
Zuckerman, Mai and Rohde. *Plant Parasitic Nematodes* (3 volumes). Academic Press, 1971.

## ACKNOWLEDGEMENTS
The line drawing, figure 4, is by the late Dr R. S. Pitcher, who introduced me to nematology. For unveiling the marvels of the lives of parasitic worms, and for his enthusiasm, teaching, guidance and life-long friendship, I shall remain ever grateful. Illustrations have been provided by: East Malling Research Station, figures 7, 12, 15, 16 and plate 7; Dr D. G. McNamara, plate 9; Rothamsted Experimental Station, figures 2, 3, 8, 14, plate 6 and the cover; the Wellcome Museum of Medical Science, figure 9 and plates 1, 2 and 3; to all of whom I extend my thanks. Other illustrations are my own.